COUNT DRACULA
AND TH...

The next night the ghost helped Dracula
out of his coffin.

1

"Still no victims," moaned Dracula.
"No one for me to bite."

"It's not fair," agreed the ghost.
"No one here for you to bite or me to scare."

Suddenly there was a knock at the door.
They both rushed downstairs.
"I'll answer it," shouted Dracula.
"This is **my** castle."

"No let me," said the ghost.
"I have to scare the victim first."

"This is **my** castle," shouted the Count.
"**I'll** open the door to the victim."
He opened the door.

"Come in, come in. Welcome."
In came a monster.

"Who are you?" asked Dracula.
"I'm Frankenstein's Monster.
F.M. to my friends."

"Go away," shouted the Count.
"We don't want monsters here.
We want victims.
What a disappointment."

"It's not fair. You let the ghost
live in your castle. Why not me?"

10

"Because it is **my** castle.
I am waiting for victims and only
ghosts and monsters turn up.
Now get lost. Go away."

The next night the Count looked
out of his window.
Outside the door was the monster.
"Go away," shouted the Count.

12

"No," shouted the monster.
"I want to live in your castle.
I won't go away."

"No victims will come if F.M. is out
there," said the ghost,
"He will scare them all away."
"What shall I do?" moaned the Count.

"Let him live here.
Let him scare victims too," said the ghost.
"All right. You down there, come on in."

"This is nice," said F.M.
"Three monsters in one castle.
We'll really scare people."